Merseyside
Painters, People & Places

Walker Art Gallery Liverpool

MERSEYSIDE

PAINTERS, PEOPLE & PLACES

Catalogue of Oil Paintings — Plates

MERSEYSIDE COUNTY COUNCIL 1978

SBN   For Complete set of 2 Volumes   901534 62 5
SBN   For this Volume   901534 61 7
Printed in Great Britain by Lund Humphries
Type: Imprint (Series 101 and 310) 8 pt, 10 pt, 12 pt, 18 pt and 24 pt
Times (Series 327) 12pt
Cover: Type Imprint and Imprint Shadow
Text: Huntsman Super White Cartridge 100 gsm and Invercarron Art 115 gsm
Cover: Chromomatt 250 gsm
Cover: Subject W. Davis, "Hale, Lancashire"
Origination by Gilchrist Bros., Leeds

Contents

BELL, Norman Martin   1907–1970

2363	Bombed Houses	322
1813	Seaside Fair Ground	323
2362	Arles	323
7259	Figures bathing	322

BENSON, Edward   1808–1863

2274	John Bramley-Moore	170

BERRIE, John Archibald Alexander   1887–1962

7131	Thomas Dowd, Lord Mayor of Liverpool	306
7132	Mrs. Dowd, Lady Mayoress of Liverpool	306
3001	George Audley	306
7014	Miss Margaret Beavan, Mayor of Liverpool	307
7135	Stuart Deacon	306

BIFFIN, Sarah   1784–1850

2559	Fanny Maria Pearson	115

BIGLAND, Percy   1858–1926

1746	Man with a Beard	260
1747	An Old Lady	260
8700	Emma Holt	260
2584	Robert Durning Holt	261
8712	Robert Durning Holt	261
7000	Rt. Hon. W. E. Gladstone	261

BISHOP, John   1810/11–1858

3002	Michael James Whitty	172
6661	John Hastings	172

BISHOP, William James   1805–1888

1722	Crazy Kate	167

BOADLE, William Barnes   1840–1916

7136	Thomas Stamford Raffles	258
2586	William James Bishop	259
3010	William Bennett	258
2558	E. Rimbault Dibdin	258
3056	Sir James Allanson Picton	258

BRITISH SCHOOL, 18th Century

BRITISH SCHOOL, late 18th Century

BRITISH SCHOOL, early 19th Century

BRITISH SCHOOL, 19th Century

BRITISH SCHOOL, late 19th Century

BROCKBANK, Albert Ernest   1862–1958

BROWN, Mather   1761–1831

DAHL, Michael   1656–1743

DALBY, David   active 1820–1840

DALBY, John   active 1840–1853

DANIELS, William   1813–1880

DAVIES, Austin Howard   living artist

DAVIS, William   1812–1873

HOLDEN, Lily   living artist

3029   The Pawnshop, Scotland Road   326

HOLT, Herbert   living artist

2411   Sam's Wife   314

HOODLESS, Harry Taylor   living artist

1488   Winter Evening on the Solway   321
3030   The Old Port, Amlwch, Anglesey   321

HORSFIELD, Nicholas   living artist

2621   Le Pollet Cliffs   328
1817   Liverpool Street   328

HUGGINS, William   1820–1884

1729   The Water Mill   140
1715   Self Portrait as a Young Man   139
1716   The Sculptor's Studio   138
3119   Portrait of a Gentleman   142
3118   The Artist's Wife   142
2563   Mrs. Coupland   141
2565   William Taylor (Banker) of Oxford   141
2564   William Peck   141
5132   Study of an Ox   143
 777   Waiting   144
7803   The Angels Ithuriel and Zephon finding Satan at the ear of Eve   140
3117   Christian and the Lions   137
1753   Christian about to turn back for fear of the lions in his approach to the Palace Beautiful   137
3120   John Deane Case, J.P. and a favourite Hunter (Tried Friends)   145
6260   William Banister of Liverpool   141
 340   On Guard   144
3116   The Artist's Wife   143
  44   Speke Hall   148
1713   Chester Cathedral   149
1739   Chester Cathedral   149
 449   Siesta—Sleeping Lions   146
1517   Old Mill and Salmon Trap on the Dee, Chester   148
 446   A Disagreement   146
 425   The Raider   152
 447   Near Helsby   150
1738   Cattle in a Landscape   151
 448   A Mixed Family   152
1714   Cheshire Meadows   150
  43   The Drinking Pool   149
 339   By the Stream   151
1510   Near Moreton   154
1712   Bebington Church   155
 652   Interior of Bebington Church   154
1754   A Lion's Head   147

LEE, John J.   active 1860–1867

LIGHTFOOT, Maxwell Gordon   1886–1911

LOCKHART, William Ewart   1846–1900

LOGSDAIL, William   1859–1944

LONSDALE, James   1777–1839

LONSDALE, James *after*

LYONS, Arthur J.   active 1891–1912

McCROSSAN, Mary   died 1934

McEVOY, Ambrose   1878–1927

851   Mrs. John Rankin   302
L33   Mrs. William Rathbone   303

MACKENZIE, Charles Douglas   1875–post 1926

2567   Rt. Hon. Thomas Price   297

MANN, James Scrimgeour   1883–1946

1530   Tide Time   304

MARSHALL, Thomas Falcon   1818–1878

7543   The Woodcutter   220
2979   John Howard visiting the Prisons in Italy in 1786   220

MARTIN, William Alison   1878/9–1936

421   A Breezy Day   310
655   Evening Glaslyn Valley   310

MAYER, Joseph   1803–1886

7620   White Tower of Seville   126
7621   Cottage Scene   126

MAYER-MARTON, George   1897–1960

3157   The Weir, Summerbridge   325

MERCIER, Captain Charles   1834–active 1879

8639   William Philip, 4th Earl of Sefton   256
7005   Oliver Holden   256

MILLINGTON, James Heath   1799–1872

7024   William Rathbone, Mayor of Liverpool   118

MOORE, George   living artist

6332   Life Machine   344

MORRISON, Robert Edward   1851/2–1924

3005   Sir James Allanson Picton   262
7133   Sir David Radcliffe   263
7483   James Eckersley Reynolds   263

RATHBONE, Harold Steward 1858–1929

REED, Stanley living artist

REID, Sir George 1841–1913

REYNOLDS, Sir Joshua *after* 1723–1792

REYNOLDS, Samuel William, Junior 1794–1872

RICHARDS, Albert 1919–1945

RICHARDS, Richard Peter 1839–1877

RIPPINGILLE, Alexander Villiers active 1815–1842

ROBERTS, Henry Benjamin 1831–1915

ROBERTSON, John Ewart 1820–1879

TOWNE, Charles   1763–1840

1240	Landscape with Cattle and Sheep; a Woman and Child crossing Rustic Bridge	74
1241	Landscape with Cattle and Sheep crossing Rustic Bridge	75
40	Landscape with Herdsman driving Cattle on the banks of a Pond	73
2313	Farm labourer driving Cattle and Sheep by a ford near a Farm	72
7642–7646	Scenes in the Life of a Racehorse	70–72
2340	Gentleman on horseback shooting Partridges	68
2341	Gentleman returning from Shooting	68
2160	Gentleman on black shooting Pony	69
2551	Gentleman on a Grey Mare	69
2312	Two Bull-Terriers attacking a Fox	76
2346	Mischief in a Park	76
2342	Shooters Resting	77
2345	Landscape with Cattle and Sheep and a Rider in conversation with a Herdsman	73
2348	A saddled Bay Hunter tethered outside a Stable	78
6107	Four horses in a Landscape	79
2314	A Groom holding unsaddled Chestnut Hunter outside a Stable	80
8635	A Grey Cob outside Croxteth Hall	82
2344	'Maghull Racecourse with a match between three horses'	82
2338	Fox hunting, Full-cry	77
2319	A Chestnut Hunter with Groom	78
2339	The Second Horse	79
2347	A Chestnut Hunter	83
1164	The Intruder	81

TOWNE, Charles, *Imitator of*

2315	A Grey Racehorse and Brown Foal	81
2343	A Grey Racehorse with Jockey up, on a Racecourse	80

TWEEDIE, William Menzies, *Ascribed to*   1826/28–1878

7012	Samuel Robert Graves	182

WALKER, Frederick   1841–1874

351	A Road Through a Cutting	219

WALSH, Sam   living artist

6194	Pin up 1963—For Francis Bacon	342
6311	Three Figures in a Warm Climate	342
6310	Emmett Dalton in Hollywood	343

WALTERS, George Stanfield   1837–1924

780	View on the Mersey with Victoria Tower	101

WALTERS, Miles   1774–1849

L143	The Pleasure yacht 'Zephyr'	100

WALTERS, Samuel   1811–1882

WALTERS, Samuel, *Attributed to*

WANE, Richard   1852–1904

WARRINGTON, Richard William   1868–1953

WATSON, William, Junior   active 1866–1921

WESTCOTT, Philip   1815–1878

WESTCOTT, Philip   1815–1878 and
ANSDELL, Richard   1815–1885

WIFFEN, Alfred K.   1896–1968

WILLIAMS, Anne   living artist

WILLIAMS, John Henry or Harry   active 1845–1877

WILLIAMSON, Daniel Alexander   1823–1903

WILLIAMSON, John   1751–1818

WILLIAMSON, John *after*

WILLIAMSON, Samuel   1792–1840

WINDUS, William Lindsay   1822–1907

WINSTANLEY, Hamlet   1694–1756

WITHEROP, Jack Coburn   living artist

WOOD, Eleanor S.   1856–active 1912

WOODLOCK, David   1842–1929

WRIGHT, John Dutton   1847–1924

WRIGHT, Richard   active 1741/6–1773

YEOMANS, Geoffrey   living artist

YOUNG, Richard   living artist

PLATES

BRITISH SCHOOL, 17th Century
1608   The Child of Hale

BRITISH SCHOOL, late 17th Century
8627   Hon. Richard Molyneux

HUYSMANS, Jacob   1633–1696
8640   Lady Mary Molyneux

BRITISH SCHOOL, late 17th Century
8631   William, 4th Viscount Molyneux

BRITISH SCHOOL, late 17th Century
8628   William, 4th Viscount Molyneux

BRITISH SCHOOL, early 18th Century
8630   Mrs. Mary Molyneux

BRITISH SCHOOL, early 18th Century
8641   (?)Richard, 5th Viscount Molyneux

BRITISH SCHOOL, early 18th Century
8638   Little Girl holding Bouquet

BRITISH SCHOOL, early 18th Century
8629   Richard, 5th Viscount Molyneux

DAHL, Michael   1656–1743
2359   Henrietta Maria, Lady Ashburnham

WINSTANLEY, Hamlet   1694–1756
L148   View of Knowsley

BRITISH SCHOOL, early 18th Century
9283   John Earle

WINSTANLEY, Hamlet   1694–1756
**139   Elizabeth, Countess of Derby and her son
Edward**

BRITISH SCHOOL, 18th Century
8637   Charles William, 1st Earl of Sefton

After REYNOLDS, Sir Joshua   1723–1792
2504   Colonel Banastre Tarleton

COTES, Francis   1725–1770
1515   Sir Robert Cunliffe, Bart.

COTES, Francis   1725–1770
1514   Lady Cunliffe

GAINSBOROUGH, Thomas 1727–1788
8780 Isabella, Viscountess Molyneux, later Countess of Sefton

PICKERING, Henry,   active 1740–1770/1
7016   Thomas Johnson

PICKERING, Henry,   active 1740–1770/1
7015   Mrs. Thomas Johnson and daughter

CADDICK
3109   Portrait of a Young Man

STUBBS, George   1724–1806
8294 James Stanley

CADDICK
3108 The Caddick Family

CADDICK
3110 Head of a Young Man

CADDICK
L139 John Gore

CADDICK, (?)William   1719/20–1794
1135   Joseph Brooks

WRIGHT, Richard, active 1741/6–1773
2164 The Fishery

BRITISH SCHOOL, 18th Century
3019 Robert Williamson

BRITISH SCHOOL, 18th Century
2506 Richard Gildart

BRITISH SCHOOL, 18th Century
2548   Thomas Bentley

BRITISH SCHOOL, 18th Century
3115   Liverpool from Tranmere Pool

BRITISH SCHOOL, late 18th Century
1740 **The Burning of Liverpool Exchange**

51

BRITISH SCHOOL, late 18thCentury
6252 The Leicester Family

TATE, William, active 1770–1806
2542 Elizabeth Knowles, Mrs. Daulby

TATE, William, active 1770–1806
2541 Daniel Daulby

IBBETSON, Julius Caesar   1759–1817
1819   Lower Rydal Waterfall

TATE, William,   active 1770–1806
9067   Mr. Tate of Toxteth Park

TATE, William,   active 1770–1806
2543   Margaret Roscoe, Mrs. Daulby

TATE, William,   active 1770–1806
9281   Miss Tate of Toxteth Park

IBBETSON, Julius Caesar   1759–1817
2529   Hugh Mulligan

CHUBBARD, Thomas   1737/8–1809
8624   A Landscape with a Bridge and Cottages

CHUBBARD, Thomas   1737/8–1809
8623   Bridge over Rapids by a Mill

After WILLIAMSON, John 1751–1818
6136 William Roscoe

WILLIAMSON, John 1751–1818
2589 Mrs. William Roscoe

WILLIAMSON, John 1751–1818
2547 William Roscoe

WILLIAMSON, John 1751–1818
2266 William Roscoe

WILLIAMSON, John   1751–1818
1542   Henry Fuseli

WILLIAMSON, John   1751–1818
3167   Five Sons of William Roscoe

WILLIAMSON,   John 1751–1818
2265   Peter Litherland

WILLIAMSON, John   1751–1818
2585   John Shepherd

WILLIAMSON, John   1751–1818
2267   Mrs. Roscoe and Child

WILLIAMSON, John   1751–1818
8707   John Durning

WILLIAMSON, John   1751–1818
8706   William Durning

WILLIAMSON, John   1751–1818
8708   Anne Durning

BRITISH SCHOOL, early 19th Century
7026 John Bridge Aspinall

BROWN, Mather 1761–1831
7041 John Bridge Aspinall

HARGREAVES, Thomas   1774–1847
3121   Francis Hargreaves

BRITISH SCHOOL, early 19th Century
2587   John Bridge Aspinall

HARGREAVES, Thomas   1774–1847
2683   Mrs. Johnson

HARGREAVES, Thomas   1774–1847
2682   Miss Freckleton

(?)ARROWSMITH, Thomas ±1772–1829
8704 Oliver Holt

(?)ARROWSMITH, Thomas ±1772–1829
8701 Young Man of the Holt Family

ARROWSMITH, Thomas ±1772–1829
8705 William Durning

ARROWSMITH, Thomas ±1772–1829
8703 Jane, wife of William Durning

ALLEN, Joseph   1770–1839
7391   Thomas, Eleanor and Anne Lance

ALLEN, Joseph   1770–1839
7393   Thomas Lance

ALLEN, Joseph   1770–1839
7392   Mrs. Thomas Lance

ALLEN, Joseph   1770–1839
8532   A Sculptor with a bust of Mr. Blundell

ALLEN, Joseph   1770–1839
3059   John Bolton

BEACH, Thomas   1738–1806
L136   John George Audley

NEWTON, Gilbert Stuart   1794–1835
2571   James Maury

BRITISH SCHOOL, early 19th Century
7001   Thomas Golightly

ALLEN, Joseph   1770–1839
9055   Peter Whitfield Brancker

TOWNE, Charles   1763–1840
2340   Gentleman on horseback shooting Partridges

TOWNE, Charles   1763–1840
2341   Gentleman returning from Shooting

TOWNE, Charles 1763–1840
2551 Gentleman on a Grey Mare

TOWNE, Charles 1763–1840
2160 Gentleman on black shooting Pony

TOWNE, Charles 1763–1840
Scenes in the Life of a Racehorse: 7642 Mare and Foal (1)

TOWNE, Charles   1763–1840
7643   The Racehorse (3)

TOWNE, Charles 1763–1840
7644 Fallen in Shafts of Huckster's Cart (6)

TOWNE, Charles 1763–1840
7645 Lying Dead in a Field (7)

TOWNE, Charles   1763–1840
7646   Carted Off (8)

TOWNE, Charles   1763–1840
2313   Farm Labourer driving Cattle and Sheep

TOWNE, Charles   1763–1840
40   Landscape with Herdsman driving Cattle

TOWNE, Charles   1763–1840
2345   Landscape with Cattle and Sheep

TOWNE, Charles   1763–1840
1240   Landscape with Cattle and Sheep

TOWNE, Charles   1763–1840
1241   Landscape with Cattle and Sheep crossing Rustic Bridge

TOWNE, Charles 1763–1840
2346 Mischief in a Park

TOWNE, Charles 1763–1840
2312 Two Bull-Terriers attacking a Fox

TOWNE, Charles   1763–1840
2342   Shooters Resting

TOWNE, Charles   1763–1840
2338   Fox hunting, Full-cry

TOWNE, Charles   1763–1840
2319   A Chestnut hunter with Groom

TOWNE, Charles   1763–1840
2348   A saddled Bay Hunter

TOWNE, Charles   1763–1840
2339   The Second Horse

TOWNE, Charles   1763–1840
6107   Four horses in a Landscape

TOWNE, Charles 1763–1840
2314 A Groom holding unsaddled Chestnut Hunter

Imitator of TOWNE, Charles
2343 A Grey Racehorse with Jockey up on a Racecourse

TOWNE, Charles, 1763–1840
1164   The Intruder

Imitator of TOWNE, Charles
2315   A Grey Racehorse and Brown Foal

TOWNE, Charles 1763–1840
2344 'Maghull Racecourse with a match between three horses'

TOWNE, Charles 1763–1840
8635 A Grey Cob outside Croxteth Hall

TOWNE, Charles 1763–1840
2347 A Chestnut Hunter

DALBY, David ±1820–1840
8636 Car and Tandem outside Croxteth

DALBY, John ±1840−1853
2326 **Racing at Hoylake**

BRITISH SCHOOL, 19th Century
2400 **Brickfield, (?)Denison Street, Liverpool**

BRITISH SCHOOL, 19th Century
949 Everton Village

PENNINGTON, John(?) 1773–1841
L142 Walton-on-the-Hill

BRITISH SCHOOL, 19th Century
137   The North Shore

BRITISH SCHOOL, 19th Century
2550   Old Plough Inn, Walton

SALOMON, Robert 1775–post 1842
479 A Sailing Ship in the Mersey

SALOMON, Robert 1775–post 1842
597 **Liverpool Town Hall, 1806**

89

SALOMON, Robert   1775–post 1842
598   View in the Mersey

SALOMON, Robert   1775–post 1842
599   American Ships in the Mersey off Liverpool

AUSTIN, Samuel   1796–1834
837   Bootle Landmarks

After AUSTIN, Samuel   1796–1834
417   The Black Rock Fort and Lighthouse, Liverpool

HUNT, Andrew 1790–1861
2937 The Estuary of the Mersey

HUNT, Andrew 1790–1861
4315 Sefton Church

HUNT, Andrew   1790–1861
866   Wallasey Pool from Seacombe Shore

HUNT, Andrew   1790–1861
5665   A Sketch of a Cornfield with Figures

BARBER, Charles   1784–1854
1757   Dovedale, Derbyshire

BARBER, Charles   1784–1854
1756   Landscape

WILLIAMSON, Samuel   1792–1840
7633   Wedgwood's Pottery, Etruria, Staffordshire

WILLIAMSON, Samuel   1792–1840
2961   Mountainous Landscape

WILLIAMSON, Samuel   1792–1840
419   Fishing boats entering Harbour

WILLIAMSON, Samuel 1792–1840
2421 Fishing boat in a heavy sea

CALVERT, Frederick ±1827–1844
1493 Shipping in the Mersey

WILLIAMSON, Samuel 1792–1840
2962 **New Brighton Shore in 1835**

DUNCAN, Edward 1803–1882
31 **Laying the Foundation Stone of Birkenhead Docks**

WILLIAMSON, Samuel 1792–1840
2285 North Shore, Liverpool

(?)WALTERS, Samuel 1811–1882
1820 The Sailing Ship 'Emma'

WALTERS, Miles 1774–1849
L143 The Pleasure yacht 'Zephyr'

WALTERS, Samuel 1811–1882
1732 Returning to Ireland, Scene off St. George's Pier, Liverpool

WALTERS, George Stanfield   1837–1924
780   View on the Mersey with Victoria Tower

WALTERS, Samuel   1811–1882
2999   The Great Gale of January 1839

WALTERS, Samuel 1811–1882
3000 The Steamship 'British Queen' in a heavy sea

WALTERS, Samuel 1811–1882
2988 The Liverpool Ship 'Bland'

WALTERS, Samuel   1811–1882
420   The 'Frankfield'

WALTERS, Samuel   1811–1882
418   S.S. 'City of Brussels'

WALTERS, Samuel 1811–1882
760   The Port of Liverpool

Studio of LAWRENCE, Sir Thomas
1769–1830
3078   Rt. Hon. George Canning, M.P.

LONSDALE, James   1777–1839
2284   General Isaac Gascoyne, M.P.

THOMPSON, T. C.   ±1778–1857
**3018   Rt. Hon. Dudley Ryder, Viscount Sandon,
M.P.**

SHEE, Sir Martin Archer   1769–1850
3130   William Roscoe

LONSDALE, James   1777–1839
3004   William Roscoe

After LONSDALE, James
3013   William Roscoe

SHEE, Sir M. A.   1769–1850
4555   William Roscoe

ILLIDGE, Thomas Henry   1799–1851
3012   Rev. William Shepherd

PHILLIPS, Sir Thomas   1770–1845
7023   George Case

PHILLIPS, Sir Thomas   1770–1845
7031   William Wallace Currie

THOMPSON, T. C.   ±1778–1857
6347   Nicholas Robinson

LONSDALE, James   1777–1839
L251   Henry Hollinshead Blundell

THOMPSON, T. C.   ±1778–1857
3015   William Wallace Currie

LONSDALE, James 1777–1839
7002 Thomas Colley Porter

LONSDALE, James 1777–1839
L249 James Aspinall

BRITISH SCHOOL, 19th Century
2557 John Naylor Wright

LONSDALE, James   1777–1839
L247   George Brown

BRITISH SCHOOL, 19th Century
L250   Joseph Brackley

BRITISH SCHOOL, 19th Century
7481   Portrait of a Liverpool sitter

HENDERSON, Cornelius   1799–1852
7020   Thomas Molyneux

HENDERSON, Cornelius   1799–1852
9140   Rev. William Shepherd

BRITISH SCHOOL, early 19th Century
7480   Joseph Williamson

BRITISH SCHOOL, early 19th Century
9263   Rev. J. B. Monk

(?)CROSTHWAITE, S.   ±1832–1841
9262   Rev. F. Iliff

BRITISH SCHOOL, 19th Century
9194   Member of the Brancker Family

(?)CROSTHWAITE, S.   ±1832–1841
2570   G. P. Day, Liverpool Newsman

RIPPINGILLE, A. V.   ±1815–1842
1139   Rev. Thomas Raffles

REYNOLDS, S. W., Jnr.   1794–1872
8720   Thomas Potter

BIFFIN, Sarah   1784–1850
2559   Fanny Maria Pearson

REYNOLDS, S. W., Jnr.   1794–1872
8702   Richard Potter

LONSDALE, James   1777–1839
9138   Thomas Stewart Traill

GEDDES, Andrew   1783–1844
2944   John Gibson

MILLINGTON, James Heath   1799–1872
7024   William Rathbone V

ILLIDGE, Thomas Henry 1799–1851
7030 Sir Joshua Walmsley

MOSSES, Alexander   1793–1837
7032   Thomas Brancker

MOSSES, Alexander   1793–1837
3063   Portrait of a Young Man

MOSSES, Alexander   1793–1837
L263   Thomas Stewart Traill

MOSSES, Alexander   1793–1837
3006   William Ewart

MOSSES, Alexander   1793–1837
2980   Blind Howard and his Grandchildren

(?)MOSSES, Alexander   1793–1837
7634   Cottage Girl

MOSSES, Alexander   1793–1837
3123   The Sculpture Boy

MOSSES, Alexander   1793–1837
7630   Expulsion of Adam and Eve

MOSSES, Alexander   1793–1837
3124   The Shrimper

MOSSES, Alexander   1793–1837
3122   The Savoyard

MAYER, Joseph   1803–1886
7621   Cottage Scene

MAYER, Joseph   1803–1886
7620   White Tower of Seville

DANIELS, William   1813–1880
7623   Samuel Mayer

DANIELS, William 1813–1880
7355 Joseph Mayer

DANIELS, William   1813–1880
7409   Portrait of a Young Man

DANIELS, William   1813–1880
650   The Brigand

DANIELS, William   1813–1880
7625   (?)Self Portrait

DANIELS, William   1813–1880
4539   Self Portrait

DANIELS, William   1813–1880
1618   A Gleaner

DANIELS, William   1813–1880
436   A Nun

DANIELS, William   1813–1880
1724   Self Portrait

DANIELS, William   1813–1880
435   Joan of Arc

DANIELS, William   1813–1880
1711   Young Girl by a Pedestal

DANIELS, William   1813–1880
3113   Chess Players

DANIELS, William   1813–1880
6367   Henry Morris

DANIELS, William   1813–1880
2561   William Parkinson

DANIELS, William   1813–1880
1752   Master Edmund Kirby

DANIELS, William   1813–1880
L137   John Stuart Dalton

DANIELS, William   1813–1880
7479   Joseph Hubback

DANIELS, William   1813–1880
1606   Elderly Man

DANIELS, William   1813–1880
1607   Elderly Woman

DANIELS, William   1813–1880
2380   The Argument

DANIELS, William   1813–1880
2562   A Young Man with a Squint

DANIELS, William   1813–1880
3114   An Italian Image Seller

DANIELS, William   1813–1880
1710   The Card Players

DANIELS, William 1813–1880
1760 **The Prisoner of Chillon**

HUGGINS, William 1820–1884
1753 Christian and the Lions

HUGGINS, William 1820–1884
3117 Christian and the Lions (sketch)

HUGGINS, William   1820–1884
1716   The Sculptor's Studio

HUGGINS, William   1820–1884
1715   Self Portrait

HUGGINS, William 1820–1884
7803 The Angels Ithuriel and Zephon finding Satan at the ear of Eve

HUGGINS, William 1820–1884
1729 The Water Mill

HUGGINS, William 1820–1884
2563   Mrs. Coupland

HUGGINS, William   1820–1884
2565   William Taylor (Banker) of Oxford

HUGGINS, William   1820–1884
2564   William Peck

HUGGINS, William   1820–1884
6260   William Banister

HUGGINS, William 1820–1884
3118 The Artist's Wife

HUGGINS, William 1820–1884
3119 Portrait of a Gentleman

HUGGINS, William 1820–1884
3116 The Artist's Wife

HUGGINS, William 1820–1884
5132 Study of an Ox

HUGGINS, William 1820–1884
777 Waiting

HUGGINS, William 1820–1884
340 On Guard

HUGGINS, William 1820–1884
3120 John Deane Case and a favourite Hunter (Tried Friends)

HUGGINS, William   1820–1884
449   Siesta—Sleeping Lions

HUGGINS, William   1820–1884
446   A Disagreement

HUGGINS, William   1820–1884
1754   A Lion's Head

HUGGINS, William   1820–1884
44   Speke Hall

HUGGINS, William   1820–1884
1517   Old Mill and Salmon Trap on the Dee, Chester

HUGGINS, William   1820–1884
1739   Chester Cathedral

HUGGINS, William   1820–1884
43   The Drinking Pool

HUGGINS, William   1820–1884
1713   Chester Cathedral

HUGGINS, William   1820–1884
447   Near Helsby

HUGGINS, William   1820–1884
1714   Cheshire Meadows

HUGGINS, William   1820–1884
339   By the Stream

HUGGINS, William   1820–1884
1738   Cattle in a Landscape

HUGGINS, William   1820–1884
448   A Mixed Family

HUGGINS, William   1820–1884
425   The Raider

HUGGINS, William   1820–1884 and BOND, W. J. J. C.   1833–1926
1621   Donkey and Foal

HUGGINS, William   1820–1884
652   Interior of Bebington Church

HUGGINS, William   1820–1884
1510   Near Moreton

HUGGINS, William 1820–1884
1712 **Bebington Church**

ANSDELL, Richard 1815–1885
2119 Shooting Party in the Highlands

ANSDELL, Richard 1815–1885
9021 The Waterloo Coursing Meeting

ANSDELL, Richard 1815–1885
8779 The Earl of Sefton and Party returning from grouse shooting, with a view of Glen Lyon, Perthshire

ANSDELL, Richard 1815–1885
8633 A Brace of Pheasants

ANSDELL, Richard 1815–1885
8189 Dead Hare

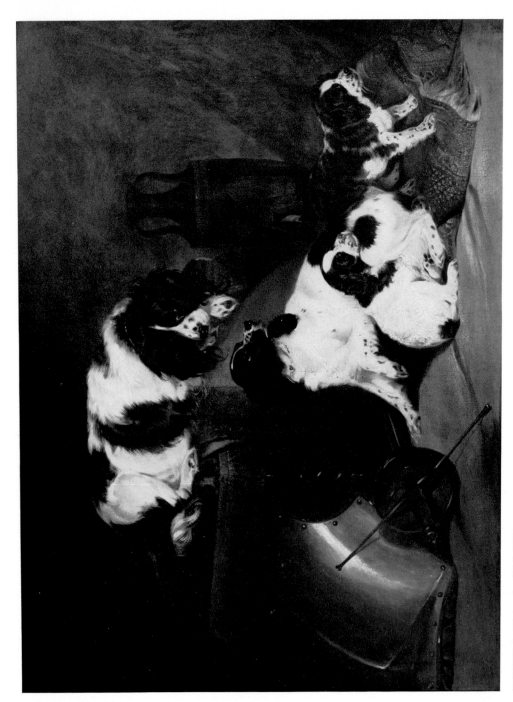

ANSDELL, Richard   1815–1885
7777   **Two Spaniels with their Pups**

ANSDELL, Richard   1815–1885
1432   A Mastiff

ANSDELL, Richard   1815–1885
6158   Jonathan Blundell, with his greyhounds

ANSDELL, Richard   1815–1885
9266   Tiny, a Manchester Terrier

ANSDELL, Richard   1815–1885 and
PHILLIP, John   1817–1867
2715   Students of Salamanca Serenading

160

ANSDELL, Richard 1815–1885
111 Stag at Bay

ANSDELL, Richard 1815–1885
7255 The Death of the Stag

ANSDELL, Richard   1815–1885
3070   The Hunted Slaves

ANSDELL, Richard   1815–1885 and CRESWICK, Thomas   1811–1869
366   The King of the Forest

ANSDELL, Richard   1815–1885
1431   The Interrupted Meal

ANSDELL, Richard   1815–1885
1433   Sheep and Lambs

EGLINGTON, Samuel   1786/7–1860
407   Trout Fishing, North Wales

EGLINGTON, James Taylor   ±1829–1868
2813   Lime Street in 1818

EGLINGTON, James Taylor ±1829–1868
940 Richard II and Bolingbroke

EGLINGTON, James Taylor ±1829–1868
2814 Old Cottage in Islington, 1822

DAWSON, Henry   1811–1878
406   The Harbour, Evening

DAWSON, Henry   1811–1878
1725   Pont Faen, near Chirk, Denbighshire

COLLINGWOOD, William   1819–1903
1465   West Hill House, Hastings

HERDMAN, William Gawin   1805–1882
L140   Lime Street, Liverpool

PELHAM, James, Snr.   1800–1874
2598   Study of an Old Man

BISHOP, William James   1805–1888
1722   Crazy Kate

GAMBARDELLA, Spiridione   ?1815–?1886
7140   Edward Rushton

BEATTIE, Robert   1810–1874
1133   James Lawrence

GAMBARDELLA, Spiridione   ?1815–?1886
2165   James Pownall

SMITH, Edward   1779/80–1849
2575   Edward Rushton

BENSON, Edward   1808–1863
2274   John Bramley-Moore

BRADLEY, William   1801–1857
1134 John Gladstone

BRADLEY, William 1801–1857
L280 John Gladstone

WESCOTT, Philip 1815–1878
2577 3rd Earl of Sefton

BISHOP, John 1810/11–1858
3002 Michael James Whitty

BISHOP, John 1810/11–1858
6661 John Hastings

WESTCOTT, Philip   1815–1878 and ANSDELL, Richard   1815–1885
8655   Charles William, 3rd Earl of Sefton

WESTCOTT, Philip 1815–1878
8709 Emma, wife of George Holt, senior, with her daughter Anne

WESTCOTT, Philip   1815–1878
8710   George Holt, senior

WESTCOTT, Philip   1815–1878
8711   George Holt, senior

WESTCOTT, Philip   1815–1878
3083   Sir John Bent

PATTEN, George   1801–1865
7025   Samuel Holme

ROBERTSON, John Ewart 1820–1879
7033 John Stewart

GORDON, Sir J. Watson   1788–1864
1138   William Brown

WESTCOTT, Philip   1815–1878
404   On the Marshes

WESTCOTT, Philip   1815–1878
9139   Joseph Brooks Yates

PATTEN, George   1801–1865
L264   William Fawcett

WESTCOTT, Philip 1815–1878
757 Rev. Augustus Campbell

WESTCOTT, Philip 1815–1878
1140 Venerable Archdeacon Brooks

PATTEN, George 1801–1865
6326 Thomas Sands

PATTEN, George 1801–1865
2167 Thomas Berry Horsfall

PHILLIP, John 1817–1867
7507 Lady Bent

PHILLIP, John 1817–1867
7506 Sir John Bent

(?)TWEEDIE, W. M. 1826/28–1878
7012 Samuel Robert Graves

ROBERTSON, John Ewart 1820–1879
8657 Joseph Robinson

ROBERTSON, John Ewart 1820–1879
8658 Mrs. Robinson

ROBERTSON, John Ewart 1820–1879
7137 James Aikin

PARTRIDGE, John 1790–1872
2981 John Gibson

After LANDSEER, Sir Edwin 1802–1873
2122 John Gibson

BOXALL, Sir William 1800–1879
3161 Mrs. W. S. Roscoe

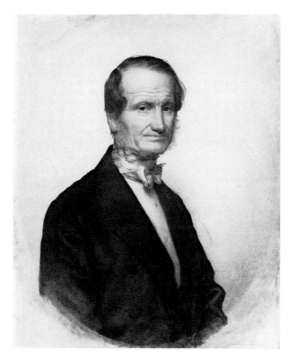

HARRIS, John   mid-19th Century
7632   Joseph Clarke

HARRIS, John   mid-19th Century
7629   Thomas Reay

HARRIS   John   mid-19th Century
7626   'Mug won't Beg'

GRANT, Sir Francis 1803—1878
6583 Georgina Naylor

GRANT, Sir Francis   1803–1878
6582   John Naylor

WINDUS, William Lindsay   1822–1907
1604   Self Portrait as a Young Man

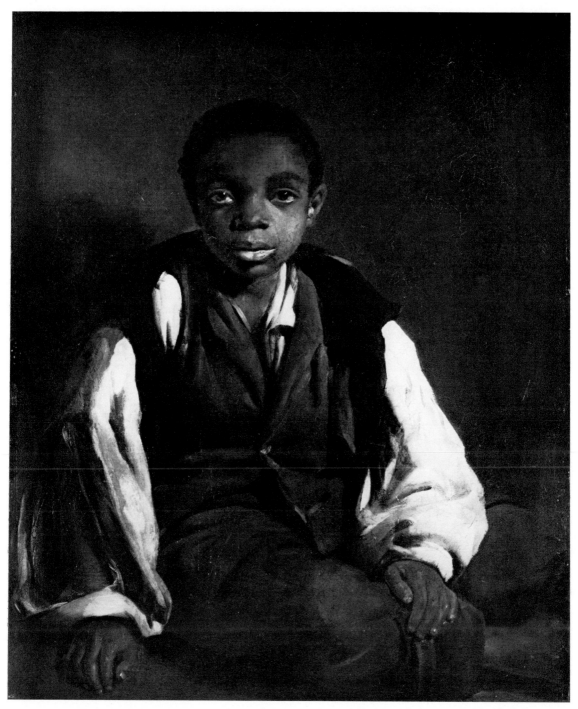

WINDUS, William Lindsay   1822–1907
1601   The Black Boy

WINDUS, W. L.   1822–1907
1595   Standing Nude Study

WINDUS, W. L.   1822–1907
1594   Seated Nude Study

WINDUS, W. L.   1822–1907
**1602   Cranmer and Catherine Howard
(sketch)**

WINDUS, W. L.   1822–1907
1591   Cranmer and Catherine Howard

WINDUS, W. L.   1822–1907
1599   Nude Study

WINDUS, W. L.   1822–1907
1598   Touchstone nominating the degrees of the lie

WINDUS, W. L.   1822–1907
1593   Morton before Claverhouse at Tillietudlem

WINDUS, William Lindsay 1822–1907
1596   Reclining Nude Study

WINDUS, William Lindsay 1822–1907
1603 **The Interview of the Apostate Shaxton, Bishop of Salisbury, with Anne Askew in Prison**

193

WINDUS, William Lindsay   1822–1907
158 Burd Helen

WINDUS, William Lindsay   1822–1907
863   The Baa Lamb: View on a Tributary of the River Duddon

WINDUS, W. L.   1822–1907
**1592   Middlemas's Interview with his Parents
(The Surgeon's Daughter)**

WINDUS, William Lindsay   1822–1907
8297   Study from Nature—The Kingfisher's Haunt, Eastham Wood

WINDUS, William Lindsay   1822–1907
1597   A Roman Patrician, A.D. 60

WINDUS, W. L.   1822–1907
480   The Young Duke

TONGE, Robert   1823–1856
1163   Landscape

TONGE, Robert   1823–1856
307   Cheshire Landscape

TONGE, Robert 1823–1856
1372 Landscape, Sefton, Lancashire

TONGE, Robert 1823–1856
2545 Landscape with distant Town

TONGE, Robert 1823–1856
308 View from Bidston Hill to the South West

DAVIS, William   1812–1873
8699   Gifts

DAVIS, William   1812–1873
2381   Pheasant and Drake

DAVIS, William   1812–1873
700   Game

DAVIS, William   1812–1873
6248   Junction of the Liffey and the Rye near Leixlip

DAVIS, William   1812–1873
L39   On the Liffey

DAVIS, William 1812–1873
L37   Bute from the High Ground

DAVIS, William 1812–1873
6247   Near Leixlip, on the Liffey

DAVIS, William   1812–1873
L38   On the Alt near Formby and Ainsdale

DAVIS, William   1812–1873
1494   Bidston Marsh

DAVIS, William   1812–1873
8724   The Rainbow

DAVIS, William   1812–1873
1495   View from Bidston Hill

DAVIS, William 1812–1873
424 Summertime

DAVIS, William 1812–1873
1115 Hale, Lancashire

Ascribed to DAVIS, William 1812–1873
8486 The Courtyard at Speke Hall

DAVIS, William   1812–1873
1121   Old Mill and Pool at Ditton

DAVIS, William 1812–1873
1116 Corner of a Cornfield

DAVIS, William 1812–1873
1146 Ploughing, Valley of the Conway

DAVIS, William 1812–1873
1508 Tree Study

CAMPBELL, James 1828–1893
6365   Girl with Jug of Ale and Pipes

CAMPBELL, James 1828–1893
1293 Waiting for Legal Advice

CAMPBELL, James 1828–1893
6246 News from My Lad

CAMPBELL, James 1828–1893
3112 Village Politicians

CAMPBELL, James 1828–1893
3062 The Old Fiddler

CAMPBELL, James 1828–1893
3111 The King's Shilling

CAMPBELL, James 1828–1893
423 The Homeward Trudge

NEWTON, John Edward   1834/5–1891
6250   Mill on the Alleyn, Denbighshire

LEE, John J.   active 1860–1867
601 Going to Market

HULME, Frederick William   1816–1884
1472   Rivington Valley

LEE, John J.   active 1860–1867
450   Bird Nesting

WALKER, Frederick 1841–1874
351 A Road Through a Cutting

MARSHALL, Thomas Falcon   1818–1878
7543   The Woodcutter

MARSHALL, Thomas Falcon   1818–1878
2979   John Howard visiting the Prisons in Italy in 1786

HUNT, Alfred William   1830–1896
718   Stybarrow Crag, Ullswater

WILLIAMS, Harry ±1845-1877
1721 Near Altcar

222

HUNT, Alfred William 1830–1896
944 **Brignall Banks**

OAKES, John Wright   1820–1887
L46   Morecambe Bay

OAKES, John Wright   1820–1887
410   Morning at Augera, Lago Maggiore

OAKES, John Wright   1820–1887
8188   The Tivey at Newcastle Emlyn, Cardiganshire

OAKES, John Wright   1820–1887
2704   A North Devon Glen—Autumn

ROBERTS, Henry Benjamin 1831–1915
1340 Creating a Sensation

ROBERTS, Henry Benjamin   1831–1915
2696   The Rehearsal

ROBERTS, Henry Benjamin   1831–1915
1118   Oliver Twist's First Introduction to Fagin

WILLIAMSON, Daniel Alexander   1823–1903
862   Sheep Resting

WILLIAMSON, Daniel Alexander   1823–1903
784   Spring, Arnside Knot and Coniston Range of Hills from Warton Crag

WILLIAMSON, Daniel Alexander   1823–1903
781   Morecambe Bay from Warton Crag

WILLIAMSON, Daniel Alexander   1823–1903
27   Spring Flowers

WILLIAMSON, Daniel Alexander   1823–1903
925   Warkworth Castle

WILLIAMSON, Daniel Alexander 1823–1903
1344 Wensleydale

WILLIAMSON, Daniel Alexander 1823–1903
924 Early Summer

BOND, W. J. J. C. 1833–1926
7463 House at Oxton

BOND, W. J. J. C. 1833–1926
1750 Raven's Fall, near Hurst Green

BOND, W. J. J. C.   1833–1926
1776   Stranded

BOND, W. J. J. C.   1833–1926
1357   Stranded

BOND, W. J. J. C.   1833–1926
696   Making the Harbour

BOND, W. J. J. C.   1833–1926
1749   On a lee shore in a gale

BOND, W. J. J. C.   1833–1926
2746   The Parting Gleam: Old St. Benet's Abbey, Norfolk

235

BOND, W. J. J. C.　1833–1926
1364　Hoylake Fishing Boat

BOND, W. J. J. C.　1833–1926
563　Ships at Anchor

BOND, W. J. J. C.　1833–1926
561　Conway Castle

BOND, W. J. J. C.   1833–1926
1365   Leasowe Shore

BOND, W. J. J. C.   1833–1926
562   On the Ogwen

BOND, W. J. J. C.   1833–1926
6257   Rhoscolyn

BOND, W. J. J. C.   1833–1926
1362   Fisherman and Spinney

BOND, W. J. J. C. 1833–1926
6256 Near Twizell Bridge, Northumberland

BOND, W. J. J. C. 1833–1926
1363 The Path to the Church

BOND, W. J. J. C. 1833–1926
3107 The Beach at Scheveningen: arrival of the fishing fleet

FINNIE, John 1829–1907
2818 Sunshine and Cloud: View near Capel Curig

FINNIE, John   1829–1907
1516   Snowdon from Capel Curig

FINNIE, John   1829–1907
2913   Close of a Stormy Day—Vale of Clwyd

FINNIE, John 1829–1907
2403 The River

FINNIE, John 1829–1907
2817 The Heart of Nature

BOND, W. J. J. C. 1833–1926
1775 Old Mill Near Rossett

FINNIE, John 1829–1907
910 The Mere

HUSON, Thomas   1844–1920
2838   A Sunny October Morning

HUSON, Thomas   1844–1920
914   When Seas are Fair and Winds are still

HUSON, Thomas   1844–1920
2975   A Midsummer Day

HAYES, Frederick William   1848–1918
1452   On the Colwyn

HAYES, Frederick William   1848–1918
596   On the Colwyn, Beddgelert

HAYES, Frederick William   1848–1918
4114   Boulders near Aberglaslyn

HARTLAND, Albert 1840–1893
2930 Moorland, near Barmouth

COOKE, Isaac 1846–1922
1796 Golden Moments

GHENT, Peter 1857–1911
911   Quiet Evening—Vyrnwy Valley

GHENT, Peter 1857–1911
2645   Nature's Mirror

RICHARDS, Richard Peter   1839–1877
2698   The Silver Cloud

RICHARDS, Richard Peter   1839–1877
2697   The Diamond Fields: View on the River Wharfe, near Bolton Abbey

SULLIVAN, William Holmes   1836–1908
2417   Harvest Moon

RICHARDS, Richard Peter   1839–1877
426   'Twixt night and day'

WATSON, William, Jnr.   ±1866–1921
1343   On the Goil, Glen Goil, Argyllshire

WATSON, William, Jnr.   ±1866–1921
1332   Morning, near Oban

WANE, Richard   1852–1904
2959   Little Gardeners

WANE, Richard   1852–1904
1373   The Lonely Watch

BRITISH SCHOOL, 19th Century
L141   S.S. 'Truthful'

GRIMSHAW, Atkinson   1836–1893
L138   The Docks, Liverpool, at night

GRIMSHAW, Atkinson   1836–1893
L24   The Custom House, Liverpool, looking South

GRIMSHAW, Atkinson   1836–1893
L23   The Custom House, Liverpool, looking North

PEARCE, Stephen   1819–1904
8634   William Philip, 4th Earl of Sefton

MERCIER, Charles   1834–±1879
8639   William Philip, 4th Earl of Sefton

MERCIER, Charles   1834–±1879
7005   Oliver Holden

DICKINSON, H. J. B.
2666   Colonel William Hall Walker on Flirt

BRITISH SCHOOL, 19th Century
7198   (Sir) Andrew Barclay Walker

BOADLE, William Barnes   1840–1916
3010   William Bennett

BOADLE, William Barnes   1840–1916
3056   Sir James Allanson Picton

BOADLE, William Barnes   1840–1916
7136   Thomas Stamford Raffles

BOADLE, William Barnes   1840–1916
2558   E. Rimbault Dibdin

258

BOADLE, William Barnes   1840–1916
2586   William James Bishop

BRITISH SCHOOL, 19th Century
7134   John Weightman

SMITH, William   19th Century
2576   William Rathbone V

BIGLAND, Percy   1858–1926
1746   Man with a Beard

BIGLAND, Percy   1858–1926
1747   An Old Lady

BIGLAND, Percy   1858–1926
8700   Emma Holt

MORRISON, R. E.   1851/2–1924
275   George Holt

BIGLAND, Percy   1858–1926
8712   Robert Durning Holt

BIGLAND, Percy   1858–1926
2584   Robert Durning Holt

BIGLAND, Percy   1858–1926
7000   Rt. Hon. W. E. Gladstone

BRITISH SCHOOL, 19th Century
7780   William Henry Watts

MORRISON, R. E.   1851/2–1924
3005   Sir James Allanson Picton

BARRETT, Jerry   ±1824–1906
1132   John Hughes

MORRISON, R. E.   1851/2–1924
7133   Sir David Radcliffe

MORRISON, R. E.   1851/2–1924
7483   James Eckersley Reynolds

MORRISON, R. E.   1851/2–1924
2166   J. G. Livingston

MORRISON, R. E.   1851/2–1924
2569   Colonel W. Hall Walker (Lord Wavertree)

MORRISON, R. E.   1851/2–1924
2681   Elderly Man

MORRISON, R. E.   1851/2–1924
1359   Sir William Bower Forwood

MORRISON, R. E.   1851/2–1924
7006   (Sir) Thomas Hughes

MORRISON, R. E.   1851/2–1924
7138   Sir Thomas Hughes

MORRISON, R. E.   1851/2–1924
7011   Edward Russell-Taylor

MORRISON, R. E.   1851/2–1924
753   Rev. Alexander Stewart

BRITISH SCHOOL, 19th Century
7484   Rev. Alexander Whishaw

BROWN, BARNES and BELL
2560   Edward Sunners

DRURY, Tony   19th Century
2590   Andrew Commins

NORBURY, Richard 1815–1886
2572 Hugh Shimmin

LEDERER, J. A. F. 1830–1910
2412 Old Man with white Beard

KIDSON, Henry Edwin 1832–1910
2591 W. G. Herdman

LEDERER, J. A. F. 1830–1910
2413 Elderly Man

After ORCHARDSON, W. Q.
3016 Sir Andrew Barclay Walker, Bart.

OULESS, W. W.   1848–1933
2573 Andrew George Kurtz

HERKOMER, H. von   1849–1914
3057 Charles MacIver

ORCHARDSON, W. Q.   1832/5–1910
149   Frederick Arthur, 16th Earl of Derby

SHANNON, J. J.   1862–1923
3007   Monsignor Nugent

LOCKHART, W. E.   1846–1900
3058   Samuel Smith, M.P.

BUKOVAC, Vlaho   1855–1923
1779   Mrs. Richard Le Doux

WOODLOCK, David 1842–1929
**2424 Feeding the Pigeons—
St. Mark's, Venice**

WOODLOCK, David 1842–1929
2423 Old Friends

WOOD, E. S. 1856–±1912
2603 William Edwards Tirebuck

PRESCOTT, C. T.   ±1890–1942
2719   Steble Fountain, William Brown Street

PRESCOTT, C. T.   ±1890–1942
2720   St. John's Market, Liverpool

PRESCOTT, C. T. ±1890–1942
2721 Underground Railway, Liverpool

PRESCOTT, C. T. ±1890–1942
2157 Water Street

PRESCOTT, C. T. ±1890–1942
1512 Bold Street from Waterloo Place

273

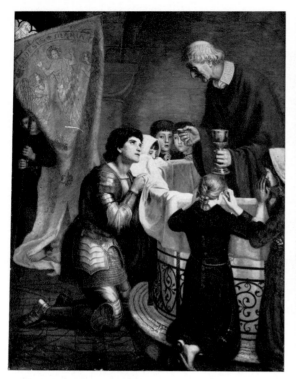

RATHBONE, Harold 1858–1929
2686 Jeanne d'Arc

RATHBONE, Harold 1858–1929
2984 The Banqueting Hall, Conway Castle

LOGSDAIL, William 1859–1944
2566 Thomas Hampson Jones

HUNT, William Holman 1827–1910
1636 Harold Rathbone

FOWLER, Robert   1850/1–1926
2915   Eve: the Voices

FOWLER, Robert   1850/1–1926
2823   Women of Phoenicia

FOWLER, Robert   1850/1–1926
2821   Ariel

FOWLER, Robert 1850/1–1926
2822 Sleeping Nymphs discovered by a Shepherd

COOKSEY, M. L. G. 1878–1943
1798 Marriage of St. Catherine

FOWLER, Robert 1850/1–1926
2819 The Annunciation

277

GARRAWAY, George Hervey   1846–1935
2949   The Florentine Poet

GARRAWAY, George Hervey   1846–1935
2958   The Madonna di San Antonio, after Titian

WARRINGTON, R. W.   1868–1953
6889   Still Life

WARRINGTON, R. W.   1868–1953
6890   Still Life with Lamp

WARRINGTON, R. W.   1868–1953
6891   Still Life

BELL, Robert Anning   1863–1933
2432   Study of a Woman's head (Fanny Dove Hamel Lister)

BELL, R. A.   1863–1933
8520   Clock

LISTER, Fanny Dove Hamel   1864–1954
8511   Left panel of frieze

BELL, Robert Anning   1863–1933
8510   The King and Queen of Hearts: centre panel of frieze

JACKSON, Enid
8512   Right panel of frieze

KELLY, Robert Talbot 1861–1935
2512 The Flight of the Khalifa after his defeat at the Battle of Omdurman, 1898

FURSE, Charles Wellington   1868–1904
9306   Cotton Trolleys

FURSE, Charles Wellington   1868–1904
2824   Unloading a Ship: Study for a Spandrel in Liverpool Town Hall

SHANNON, Charles Haslewood   1865–1937
6578   Mrs. Elizabeth Dowdall

SHANNON, Charles Haslewood   1865–1937
6579   Lady with a Cyclamen: Hon. Mrs. H. Chaloner Dowdall

HAY, James Hamilton   1874–1916
2511   The Lady in the Japanese Gown—Portrait of Miss Enid Rutherford

HAY, James Hamilton 1874–1916
714 The Lovers

HAY, James Hamilton 1874–1916
2408 The Falling Star

HAY, James Hamilton   1874–1916
2407   Cornish Seascape

DAWBARN, J. Y.   1856–1943
437   Oppidi Opulentia

PEDDER, John 1850–1929
8601 Sheep in a Field

ROYLE. Herbert F. 1870–1958
1330 Haymaking Weather, Tawd Vale

McCROSSAN, Mary   died 1934
617   Umbrellas and Barges, Venice

GRANT, James Ardern   1885–1973
1631   George Harris

McCROSSAN, Mary   died 1934
668   White Gigs, Moonlight

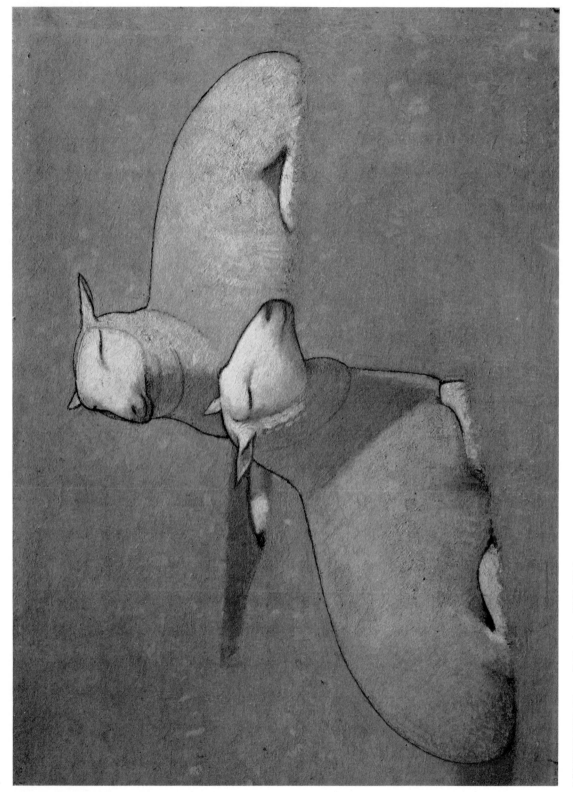

LIGHTFOOT, Maxwell Gordon 1886–1911
1719 **Study of Two Sheep**

LIGHTFOOT, Maxwell Gordon 1886–1911
1124 **Flowers in a Blue and White Vase**

LIGHTFOOT, Maxwell Gordon 1886–1911
7256 **Knapweed, Thistles and Flowers in a Vase**

LIGHTFOOT, Maxwell Gordon 1886–1911
1720 View of Conway from above Gyffin

LIGHTFOOT, Maxwell Gordon 1886–1911
2366 Landscape, Abergavenny

WRIGHT, James Dutton 1847–1924
3103 The Old St. George's Dock: Site of the present Royal Liver Building

JENKINS, David Charles 1867–1916
2939 The Sands, New Brighton

LYONS, Arthur J. ±1891–1912
3079 The Inaugural Banquet of the 41st Autumn Exhibition, 1911

NEALE, George Hall ±1883–1940
3022 Sir William Bower Forwood

NEALE, George Hall ±1883–1940
7595 Edward Lewis Lloyd

COPEMAN, Constance Gertrude   1864–1953
1800   John Finnie

NEALE, George Hall   ±1883–1940
89   Self Portrait

NEALE, George Hall   ±1883–1940
3014   W. J. J. C. Bond

NEALE, George Hall ±1883–1940
46 First Steps

NEALE, George Hall ±1883–1940
7195 Sir Edward, afterwards Lord Russell

NEALE, Maud Hall ±1889–1938
7196 Lady Russell

REID, Sir George   1841–1913
2599   Rev. John Watson, D.D.

BACON, J. H. F.   1865–1914
3008   T. P. O'Connor, M.P.

BEAUMONT, F. S.   1861–after 1952
3009   Sir Alfred Lewis Jones

MACKENZIE, C. D.   1875–post 1926
2567   Rt. Hon. Thomas Price

PALMER, Lynwood   1866/7–1941
2629   Colonel William Hall Walker, M.P., on Buttercup

After SARGENT, J. S.   1856–1925
955   Lord Wavertree

After ORPEN, William   1878–1931
7017   Edward, 17th Earl of Derby

COPNALL, Frank Thomas   1870–1949
3020   Sir William Bowring, Bart.

COPNALL, F. T.   1870–1949
1801   Sir Roger de Poitou

COPNALL, F. T.   1870–1949
3011   Frederick C. Bowring

COPNALL, F. T.   1870–1949
3021   E. Rimbault Dibdin

COPNALL, F. T.   1870–1949
1507   My wife with Michael

COPNALL, F. T.   1870–1949
953   Henry A. Cole

COPNALL, F. T.   1870– 1949
7482   William Denton

SALISBURY, F. O.   1874–1962
954   John Lea

SALISBURY, F. O.   1874–1962
7129   Frank Campbell Wilson

HINCHLIFFE, R. G.   1868–1942
7139   John Morris

SALISBURY, F. O.   1874–1962
7128   Mrs. Wilson

KERR-LAWSON, J. 1865–1939
2592 Mrs. Thomas Brocklebank

HENRY, George 1859–1943
241 Mrs. George Holt

McEVOY, Ambrose 1878–1927
851 Mrs. John Rankin

McEVOY, Ambrose   1878–1927
L33   Mrs. William Rathbone

MANN, James Scrimgeour 1883–1946
1530 Tide Time

BROCKBANK, A. E. 1862–1958
7142 Captain Cecil Heywood-Brunner

PENN, W. C. 1877–1968
8485 Eileen and Harry Chrimes

BROCKBANK, Albert Ernest   1862–1958
6108   Back Goree

PENN, W. C.   1877–1968
2707   The Happy Infant

HINCHLIFFE, R. G.   1868–1942
600   A Water Nymph

BERRIE, J. A. A. 1887–1962
7131 Thomas Dowd

BERRIE, J. A. A. 1887–1962
7132 Mrs. Dowd

BERRIE, J. A. A. 1887–1962
7135 Stuart Deacon

BERRIE, J. A. A. 1887–1962
3001 George Audley

BERRIE, J. A. A. 1887–1962
7014 Miss Margaret Beavan

PENN, W. C. 1877–1968
7130 Bruton W. Eills

PENN, W. C. 1877–1968
7035 Sir Sydney Jones

HALLIDAY, E. I.
8466 R. R. Bailey

PRESTON, Edward Carter 1884–1965
1072 Daphnis and Chloe

HALLIDAY, Edward Irvine
9304 Athena and Arachne

HALLIDAY, Edward Irvine
2406　Dr. William Brogdon Paterson

HALLIDAY, Edward Irvine
9305　Hilary of Poitiers

MARTIN, William Alison   1878/9–1936
421   A Breezy Day

MARTIN, William Alison   1878/9–1936
655   Evening Glaslyn Valley

PENN, William Charles   1877–1968
477   Cynicht

SHARPE, Charles William   1881–1955
1453   Hilbre

COPNALL, Teresa   1882–1972
1451   A Mixed Bunch

REED, Stanley
2370   Danae

BURKE, Thomas   1906–1945
1103   The Student

GILL, Eric Peter
3162 Prenton Claypits

KAUFMANN, Wilhelm   born 1895
1110 William Armstrong

SMITH, George Grainger   1892–1961
2684   Snowden from Capel Curig

HOLT, Herbert
2411   Sam's Wife

SMITH, George Grainger   1892–1961
1089   The Enemy Raid, May 3rd 1941

WIFFEN, Alfred K.   1896–1968
7004   Jet of Iada

RICHARDS, Albert   1919–1945
8727   Seacombe Ferry in Wartime

PAICE, Philip Stuart   1884–1940
411   Rock Ferry, Cheshire

ALBERT RICHARDS.

RICHARDS, Albert   1919–1945
8728   The Seven Legends: Self Portrait

RICHARDS, Albert   1919–1945
2371   Sappers erecting Pickets in Snow

RICHARDS, Albert   1919–1945
2601   Holland: Cold Holland

RICHARDS, Albert 1919-1945
2600 Holland: The Flooded Maas

319

WITHEROP, Jack Coburn
3159 Tin Mines, Cornwall

WITHEROP, Jack Coburn
2377 Fishing Nets, St. Ives

HOODLESS, Harry Taylor
1488 Winter Evening on the Solway

HOODLESS, Harry Taylor
3030 The Old Port, Amlwch, Anglesey

BELL, Norman Martin   1907–1970
7259   Figures Bathing

BELL, Norman Martin   1907–1970
2363   Bombed Houses

BELL, Norman Martin   1907–1970
2362   Arles

BELL, Norman Martin   1907–1970
1813   Seaside Fair Ground

DOUGLAS, Sheila
1487 Pennine Landscape

OLIVER, Charles William
1489 In a Kitchen

324

MAYER-MARTON, George 1897–1960
3157 The Weir, Summerbridge

TIMMIS, Robert 1886–1960
1113 The Two Jugs

HOLDEN, Lily
3029   The Pawnshop, Scotland Road

GRIFFITH, Edward Hales
3155   Saturday Night

YEOMANS, Geoffrey
1114   Outdoor Cafe Scene

KEATES, John Gareth
423   Derelict Station

HORSFIELD, Nicholas
2621   Le Pollet Cliffs

HORSFIELD, Nicholas
1817   Liverpool Street

328

KENNERLEY, George
3156 Liverpool Landscape

KENNERLEY, George
7400 Iris (Homage to Van Gogh)

BALLARD, Arthur
3147　Farm

BALLARD, Arthur
1102　Children Playing

BALLARD, Arthur
1812　Non-Figurative Painting No. 2

STEVENSON, William Lennie
1818 Milan

SUTCLIFFE, Stuart   1940–1962
6253 Hamburg Painting No. 2

BUTLER, Anthony
1814 Landscape

BUTLER, Anthony
3170 Fish on the Shore

GRAHAM, Henry
1816   Welsh Landscape

BUTLER, Anthony
3154   Web

DAVIES, Austin Howard
1105   The Forest Fungus

PERCIVAL, R. M.
3158   Mother and Child

DAVIES, Austin Howard
1815 Under the Brown Hill

PERCIVAL, Robert Murdoch
1111 Flower Boxes

335

HUGHES, Margaret
6181   Garden, January, 1963

HUGHES, Margaret
2365   Old Man

HERITAGE, John
3028   Landscape No. 2

HERITAGE, John
8279   Pope in a Car

JARDINE, George Wallace
6368   Sea Change

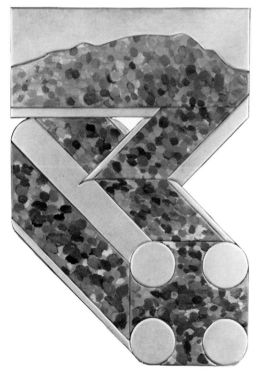

RAE, Robin
6574   Caradoc

JARDINE, George Wallace
7764 Full fathom five

YOUNG, Richard
6966 Interior with Figure

YOUNG, Richard
6364 Chandelier

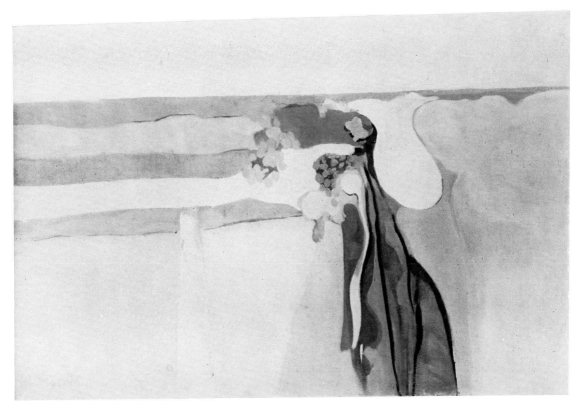

SAVAGE, Deirdre
6907   Marsh Landscape, II

SAVAGE, Deirdre
6906   Marsh Landscape, I

WALSH, Sam
6194　Pin up 1963—For Francis Bacon

WALSH, Sam
6311　Three Figures in a Warm Climate

WALSH, Sam
6310   Emmett Dalton in Hollywood

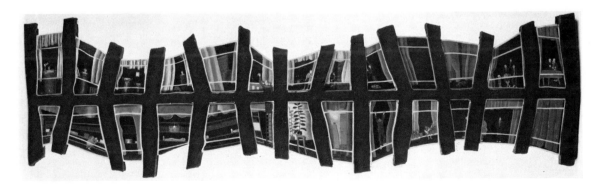

WILLIAMS, Anne
7583   Windows

COX, Reg
6305 Portrait of a Typo Man

EDKINS, John   1931–1966
6180 Nomex

MOORE, George
6332 Life Machine

EDKINS, John 1931–1966
6306 Seven Answers

COCKRILL, Maurice
8574   Two Windows/Two People

HENRI, Adrian
6575   Salad Painting VI

COCKRILL, Maurice
8722 Sudley

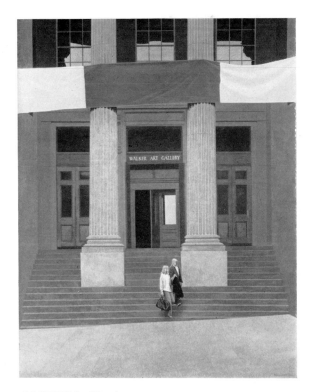

COCKRILL, Maurice
8828 The Walker Art Gallery

BAUM, John
9202 Windermere House